The REAL thing
(all my own impressive work)

This book is dedicated
to my lovely friends, who are
ALL excellent at making things:

Sarah, Ali, Vicky, Zoe,
Tracey, Jo & Lucy
xxxxx

Published in the UK by Scholastic, 2021
Euston House, 24 Eversholt Street, London, NW1 1DB
Scholastic Ireland, 89E Lagan Road, Dublin Industrial Estate,
Glasnevin, Dublin, D11 HP5F

SCHOLASTIC and associated logos are trademarks
and/or registered trademarks of Scholastic Inc.

First published in the UK in 2019

Text & illustration © Liz Pichon Ltd, 2019

The right of Liz Pichon to be identified as the author and illustrator
of this work has been asserted by her under the Copyright,
Designs and Patents Act 1988.

ISBN 978 0702 30163 6

A CIP catalogue record for this book is available from the British Library.

Printed by CPI Group (UK) Ltd, Croydon, CR0 4YY
Paper made from wood grown in sustainable
forests and other controlled sources.

10

www.scholastic.co.uk

MEGA

MAKE AND

DO

AND STORIES TOO

BY Liz Pichon

Ant resting...

The HALF-TERM HOLIDAY

is coming up next week and
EVERYONE in the whole school is just a
little bit ... ➡️

Yippee!

3

It takes a while for our class to settle down. Marcus won't sit still and keeps JUMPING around.

"HEY, TOM! TOM!

I'm doing something in the holidays that would be your DREAM.

DO YOU WANT TO KNOW WHAT IT IS?" he says loudly at me.

"Nah, not really."
Then I turn towards AMY and ask her a question instead.

"**W**hat are you doing for half-term, **AMY?**"
This annoys Marcus a lot, I can tell.

"**HANG ON** - I haven't told you what
<u>**I'M**</u> doing yet. Trust me, **you'll** <u>really</u> want
to know."

 "I've already been to CHOCOLATE
WORLD, Marcus," I remind him.

"I'm not going there - it's something
WAY better than THAT," he says.
Then he waits for us both to guess.

But we don't.

"Do you remember June?" AMY asks me.

"June? Oh yeah, her dad lives next door. She ALWAYS pulls stupid faces at me, and WORSE than that, she doesn't even like DUDE 3.

I mean, THAT'S unbelievable, right?

June is SO ANNOYING," I say as it's all coming back to me now.

 "She's my friend. Our dads are friends too, so I'm going to her house one day as she's back for half-term. I thought as you live next door you might want to hang out, or maybe not as June's so annoying," AMY tells me.

(HOW was I supposed to know that they were friends?)

"So when I said June was annoying ... she might have changed," I add, trying to make it sound better.

(ALTHOUGH I bet she still doesn't like DUDE3.)

Speaking of ANNOYING, Marcus is desperate for us to guess what he's up to and

 BLURTS OUT...

I'M going to HAVE to tell you because I can't WAIT!

"You'd better be *quick* before the lesson starts," I point out as Mr Fullerman's already standing up.

OK - I'M going to be GOING TO...

(Too late...)

"PAY ATTENTION, Class 5F. You **all** need to write this down in your homework book, please."

(GROAN...)

"Over the holidays, your homework is ..."

I'm not setting any homework THIS holiday. I'd like you all to have a break! Please keep UP your reading, and if you feel like writing anything that's fine too.

ENJOY YOUR FREE TIME."

The WHOLE cLAss

is IN **SHOCK.**

"Did Mr Fullerman really say NO homework?" AMY asks.

"I think he did!" I say.

"NO HOMEWORK..." Marcus repeats.
It takes a while for the NEWS to sink in.

"You all seem VERY pleased about that! ALSO, please don't forget that the first Monday after the holiday is an INSECT DAY, OK?"

The class sound pretty excited and **lots** of kids are saying "YES!" I join in with an **AIR** punch as well.

"THIS IS GREAT! We have no homework AND there's an **INSECT** day as well!" I tell **AMY**, who looks at me like I'm odd.

"Say that again, Tom?" she asks.

"INSECT day – or a NATURE day where we look at insects. Mark Clump will probably bring something weird in, so it should be fun, right?" Marcus Meldrew starts LAUGHING.

"What's so FUNNY?" I ask him.

"YOU ARE! Insect day!"

He's in hysterics now, which is a  Ha! Ha!

bit over the top. When Leroy walks past

our desk Marcus tells him as well.

"Tom thinks we're having

an INSECT day!"

 "Aren't we?" Leroy asks.

"Not you too!" Ha! Ha! Ha!

Marcus is off again.

"It's actually INSET day, Tom.

It means the teachers do other things that day,

so we don't have to come in to school,"

AMY explains, which STILL sounds OK to me!

"That's BRILLIANT!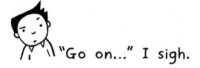
Another day off school and NO homework!"
(This is looking like an EXCELLENT half-term
already.)

"Do you want to know what I'm doing, then?"
Marcus manages to say when he stops LAUGHING.

"Go on..." I sigh.

"My aunt's getting a PUPPY and I'm
going with her to collect it. She's letting me
name it. 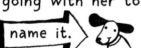 I TOLD you it would
be your dream!"

 Marcus is right. I would l♥ve to do
that. "Maybe when Delia grows up and
leaves home I can finally get a dog,"
I say.

"I've got a **DOG** already, Tom,"

Marcus says, smiling at me.

"I know..." His dog is tiny, but

very **strong**. Marcus likes to pretend that

he's in control, but I've seen him over the park

and it doesn't look that way to <u>me</u>.

Wait!

"I walk Rooster sometimes. It's almost like

having my own dog," I tell him.

I can't blame Marcus for being excited

about a puppy - I would be too.

I'm really looking forward to having  a NICE, relaxing half-term.

☆ Doing NO homework

High five

☆ Hanging out with Derek

☆ Eating snacks

☆ Doodling (obviously)

☆ Playing a few tricks on Delia (has to be done)  BOO! AGH!

☆ Visiting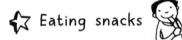

Hi, Tom!

☆ Reading my books and **COMICS**

☆ Playing with Rooster

 It's going to be a MEGA break!

When I get home, I tell Mum about having NO homework for the WHOLE of the half-term, and she looks almost as SHOCKED as I was.

"HALF-TERM? Isn't that the week <u>after</u> next, Tom?" Mum asks me.

"That's not what Mr Fullerman said when we left school today," I say.

Mum checks the calendar and does a lot of sighing and muttering. Then she goes to see Dad in the shed. (Sigh...)

 When Delia comes back from college, I take the opportunity to tell her how much FREE time I have. Her college doesn't have a HALF-TERM break like me.

It's always *FUN* to remind her of that.

"**I**'m on my lovely holiday now.
I'll be mostly RELAXING while
you're not here and enjoying the
peace and quiet. I might do some doodling
or make another one of **THESE!**"
I take out my WOOLLY monster
and dangle it in front of Delia's
face (not touching it, just near enough to
annoy her).

"Take it away, Tom. I think Mum and Dad got
your half-term mixed up."
She points to the calendar where the WRONG
week is highlighted as my holiday.

"I'll be at college, so I'm <u>not</u>
looking after you," Delia tells me.

"That's a relief," I say.

Then I swing my woolly
monster around a bit more.
"I can make you one if you want?"
I tell Delia happily.

"Thanks, it's just what I need,"

Delia says, surprisingly.

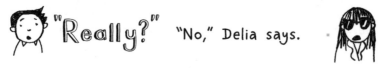

"Really?" "No," Delia says.

I'll make her one anyway.

(I am a nice brother.)

I made a sign

My

MEGA
HALF-TERM
PLAN.

19	20	21	22	23	24	25
		Tom's Half-Term				
26	27	28	29	30	31	

Someone (Dad) wrote the WRONG week on the calendar for my half-term and Mum has to go in to work.

"I can't change anything NOW," Mum says, holding her head.

Dad's at home but says he's got lots to do as well.

 "How about I ask my friends over to watch films and eat snacks with me?" I suggest helpfully.

"That's fine, Tom, but you can't do that for the whole week," Dad tells me. (I disagree.)

After a LOT of discussion about what to do, Mum and Dad make a few phone calls.

 Favour...

(But most of my friends are either busy or away.)

"How about your friend Marcus? He could come here, then you could go to his," Mum suggests.

I'm less enthusiastic about this, until I remember the **PUPPY**.

"I'll go over on the day he's picking UP a puppy!" I say.

"I'll ask," Mum says – but no one's answering his phone. I'm almost disappointed.

 No one's there, Tom.

Awwwww.

EVENTUALLY (it takes a while) Mum and Dad make a plan for the week and stick it on the fridge.

(It looks complicated.)

Derek's away visiting his granny, but at least I'll see him in a few days' time.

I'll definitely be hanging out with THE FOSSILS. But not The Wrinklies as they're away scuba diving.

(Of course they are.)

 I start (thinking) about what Marcus could call his aunt's puppy.

Hmmmmm...

I have SO many ideas!

DOG WORD SEARCH

I wonder if he'll
pick one of these...

FIDO   NIPPER
REX   BELLA
DAISY   COCO
POPPY   MAX

YUM

S	D	V	E	U	T	T	J	I	R
E	A	Y	G	B	H	N	R	D	E
R	I	P	U	E	N	L	I	L	X
F	S	P	O	B	K	W	B	L	Q
T	Y	O	N	I	P	P	E	R	F
F	A	P	A	T	A	L	L	E	B
I	F	L	J	D	C	K	S	A	P
D	L	E	D	S	G	O	E	D	I
O	T	U	P	E	L	I	C	T	E
R	B	T	U	M	A	X	H	O	S

HOLI

DAY!

Colour it in!

How to draw Rooster

Don't worry if you make a mistake!

Help Marcus through the maze

Draw Mr Fullerman

... with OTHER HAIRSTYLES?

Wobble
hair
HA, HA!

Ha! Ha!

(Go on ... have a go!)

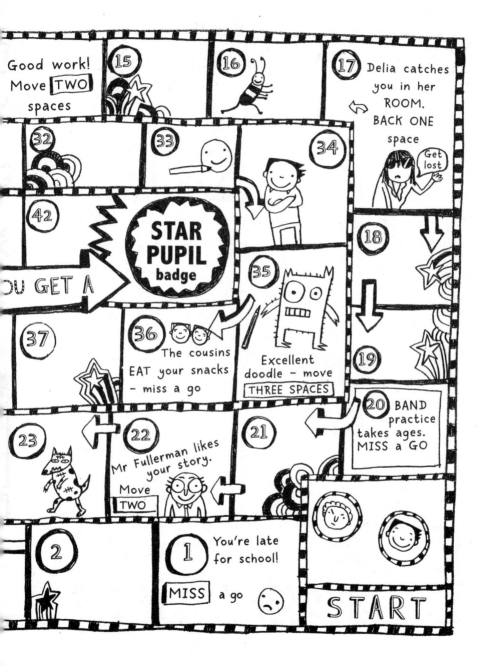

$\mathbb{M}$ake a Woolly **MONSTER**

1. Take two empty toilet rolls and some wool.

2. Tie the rolls together with wool.

3. Take your wool and wrap it around the rolls.

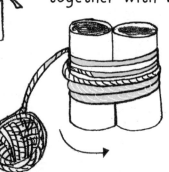

The more wool you use, the BIGGER your monster.

4. Then put your wool between your toilet rolls

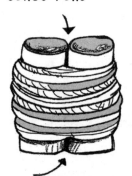

5.
Make sure you leave a LONG piece of wool to tie it together, then tie the knot as tightly as you can.

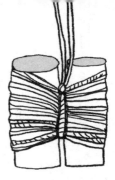

6. This bit is tricky but try and keep the long piece of wool in the MIDDLE of the wool.

7. GET ADULT HELP WITH CUTTING! BE CAREFUL WITH SCISSORS.

Cut the wool along the top.

8. GENTLY tighten the LONG piece of wool.

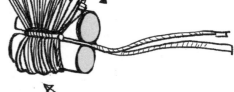

Now cut the other side.

9. Carefully take out the toilet rolls, then tighten the knot until it starts to look like this:

10. Then tie the long piece together. Fluff your woolly ball out a bit more.

Spread out the
wool as evenly
as you can to
make a ball.

Snip off any
long bits of
wool.

If you have some paper and glue or
white stickers – draw some eyes and a
mouth, then cut them out and STICK
them on your monster.

Or just keep it as a pom-pom!

Here's one I made earlier!

IMPORTANT MESSAGE!
The wool WILL come out if you pull it.
So it's not a toy for babies, young
children or animals.

Doodle space

MY HOLIDAY

I'm lying in bed enjoying NOT having to get up when Dad comes *BARGING* in and says...

"But I'm on holiday," I point out.

"I know, but you're going to work with Mum today. I'm out as well so we can't be late. Bring a few things with you – I'll be back in a second," Dad tells me.

I get up and pack a bag.

"It's a bit FULL," Dad says when he comes back. He starts to take important things out. "Why do you need a rain shaker and a sock puppet?"

"Why not?"

"Old crisp packets? What's that about?"

"It's my collection. I might add to it today," I explain while getting dressed.

(I put a few things back in when he's not looking.) ☺

We both head downstairs where Mum's already looking a bit **STRESSED**.

 "Quickly – let's go, Tom. We can pick up some breakfast on the way," she tells me and suddenly I'm

because breakfast from a café is a TREAT, <u>AND</u> when Mum's in a rush, she lets me get whatever I want.

☺ Result!

? I choose two thick blueberry pancakes with a tiny pot of maple syrup, a drink and a banana. This is a very good start to my HOLIDAY.

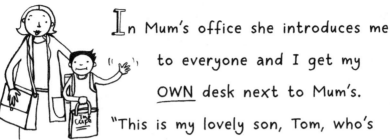

In Mum's office she introduces me to everyone and I get my OWN desk next to Mum's.

"This is my lovely son, Tom, who's come to HELP me today."

I do lots of smiling and saying hello.

"I'm sorry, we didn't have time for breakfast at home," Mum explains as I take out my food. (I'm not sorry because my pancakes look YUM!)

"Try not to make a mess, Tom.

I'm just going to a meeting," Mum tells me. I do a thumbs up.

I take a big mouthful of pancake when a lady asks, "Ooo, what kind of pancakes are those?"

"Blueberry," I say and knock over my pot of syrup.

I don't spill it all - luckily.

Covering up the syrup with some paper I find on Mum's desk does the trick.

No one can see it now,

so that's GOOD. :)

Then I finish off the last bit of pancake and sort through my bag. Hmmmmm...

"What shall I do first?" I mutter.

"Hi, Tom. There's some BIG sheets of scrap paper over here that you can help yourself to," a man in the office tells me.

GREAT!

I say, as that gives me another IDEA.

I'll make **PAPER BANGERS** to start with. I fold a few up and then decide I should really test them all out to make sure they work properly...

And they DO!

BANG

BANG

B

TOM?

Mum comes out to see what the noise is.

So I show her again.

ANG!

No one in Mum's office can believe
I can make so much noise with just paper!
So I show them how to make one. This is a
good use of my time. I think I'm going to enjoy
myself today after all...

How to make a PAPER BANGER

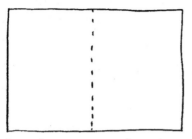

1. Take a piece of A3 paper.

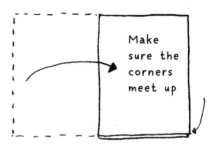

Make sure the corners meet up

2. Fold in half.

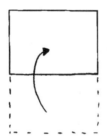

3. Then fold in quarters.

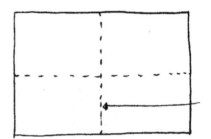

4. Then UNFOLD the paper. There should be nice fold marks now.

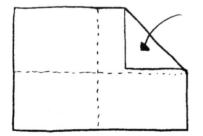

5. Fold down the corner to meet the middle fold line.

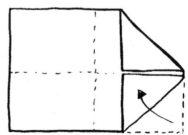

6. Do the same with every corner.

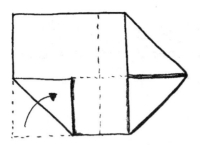

7.

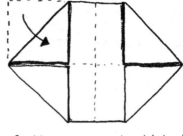

8. Your paper should look like this.

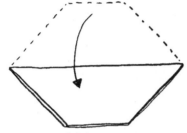

9. Now fold the paper in half, with the flaps inside.

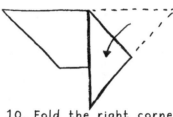

10. Fold the right corner to the middle.

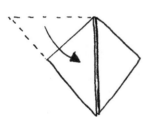

11. Then repeat on the other side.

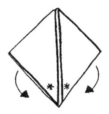

12. Fold the whole banger in half, hold the corners marked, then flick it down HARD.

Air catches under here to make a BANG!

BANG!

How to make a rain stick/shaker

Lid →

① Take an EMPTY crisp tube and make sure the inside is clean. Give it a good wipe to get rid of any crisp crumbs. Take off the lid.

② To decorate your shaker, measure a piece of paper to fit around the outside of the tube.

Like this →

③ Then colour in the paper and put it to one side.

④ Take some dry rice and a plastic funnel and put the funnel into the top of the tube. Then pour in the rice – don't

RICE

overfill it or the shaker won't make a good noise.

5 Once that's done, you'll need to tape the lid back on very securely with lots of tape so it doesn't fall off.

Tape

Tape

Don't overfill.
Up to about here.

6 You can use a glue stick to cover the side of the tube, then wrap the paper round the tube and stick with tape.

Now SHAKE!

How to make a PAPER CROCODILE

(Why not?)

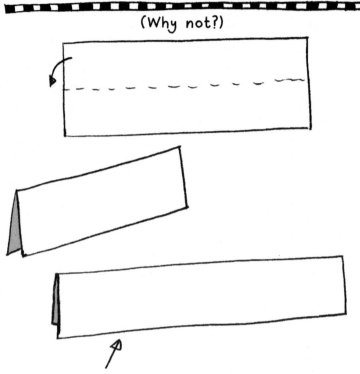

Draw a crocodile shape

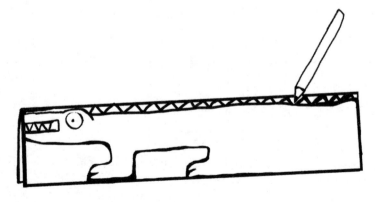

Colour in your croc on both sides.
You can use coloured paper too.

Cut both sides of the paper together around
the feet of your croc.
(Don't cut the fold, though!)

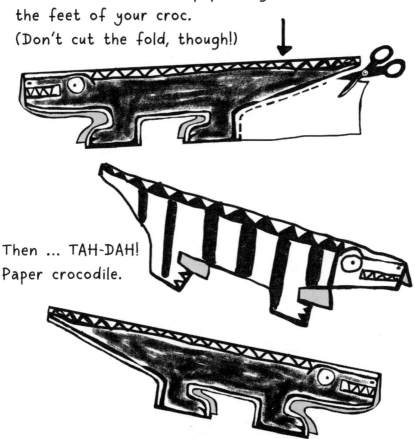

Then ... TAH-DAH!
Paper crocodile.

I do a BANANA doodle to
keep myself busy.

Blank bananas to doodle on

How to do
a BANANA doodle

Take a banana and a cocktail stick
(mind the sharp end).

Carefully push the stick into the banana
skin - not
too deeply.

Where you make a hole it will turn black.
You can do a doodle like this quite quickly.

Don't leave the banana too long before you eat it.
(They go mouldy
and the doodle will go darker and darker.
Yuck.)

How to make a
PAPER PALM TREE

(So useful.)

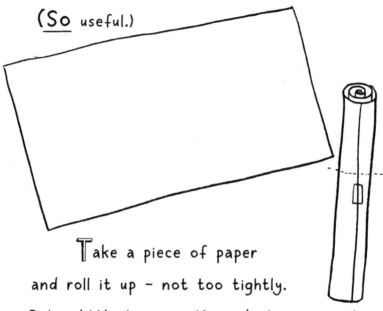

Take a piece of paper
and roll it up - not too tightly.
Put a little tape on the side to secure it.
Then carefully cut with scissors
down through all the paper

strips like this.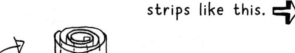

 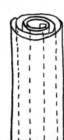

Then hold the centre of the paper and gently pull the palm leaves up and spread them out.

Pull them as far as you can to make the shape of a palm tree.

Use more tape to make it secure, and then...

Push up

TA-DAH!
Your palm tree is
DONE!

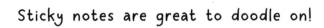
Sticky notes are great to doodle on!

With some of my STICKY NOTES I make a FLIP book. HERE'S HOW:

Decide what you want to draw on a rough piece of paper first. (Try something simple to begin with!) Here's how to do Mr Fullerman's face with BEADY EYES.

In the corner of each note, starting at the back, draw your first face.

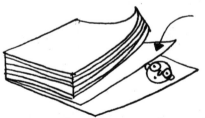

Then on the second note, TRACE over the face and move the eyes and mouth slightly – like picture 2.

Keep adding the drawings and moving the eyes around on every NOTE.

It does take a WHILE, but when you've drawn on quite a few, FLICK through the book to see how he's moving. The more pictures you draw, the better it will work.

Here's some other ideas to try:

A STICK MAN jumping.

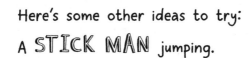

Delia being hit by mud!

How to make a POP-UP card

A4 paper

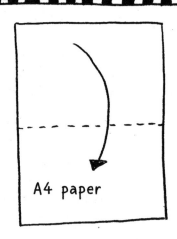

A4 paper

Then OPEN UP and fold in half THIS way.

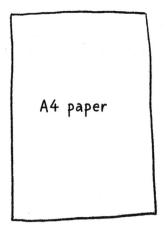

Fold down corner <u>A</u> ...

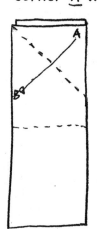

... to corner B, like this.

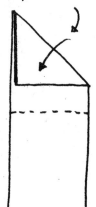

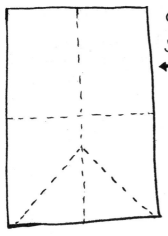

OPEN up your paper so you have all these <u>FOLDS</u>.

FOLD in half so your triangle shape is inside the card.

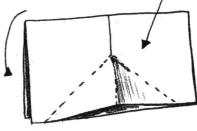

This bit is fiddly! You need to make your triangle shape fold UPWARDS inside your card. Use the paper folds to help you.

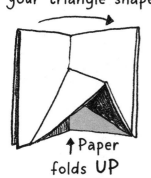

↑ Paper folds <u>UP</u>

Your card should look like this when you fold it closed.

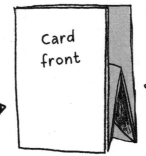

Card front

Then decorate your card. →

Fold inside

Here's the inside of the card with your triangle 'POP'-UP.

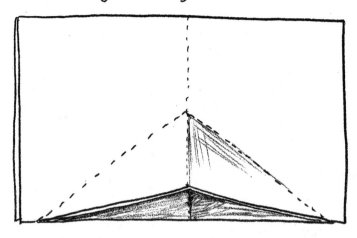

If you draw an arrow <u>ON</u> the triangle, it will look like it's popping **up**.

Here's an ant on the
front of the card!

Then inside use the
TRIANGLE shape like a
mountain!

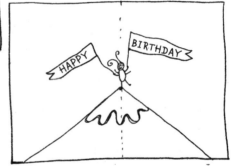

Just a note
to say ...

Here's a thank-you
card idea too.

How to make a PICTURE FRAME

Take an A4 sheet of paper and make a SQUARE by folding corner A to B – like this.

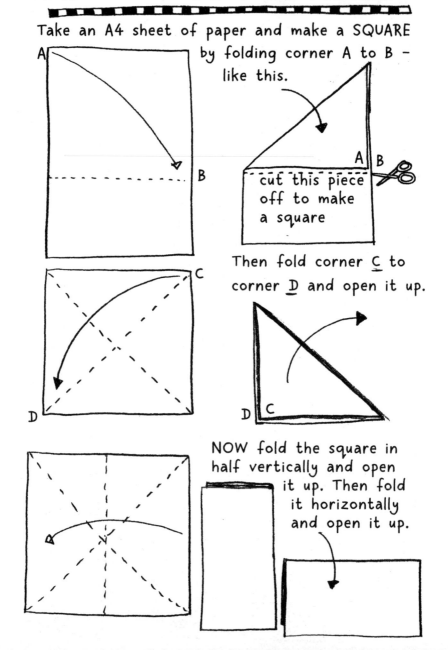

cut this piece off to make a square

Then fold corner C to corner D and open it up.

NOW fold the square in half vertically and open it up. Then fold it horizontally and open it up.

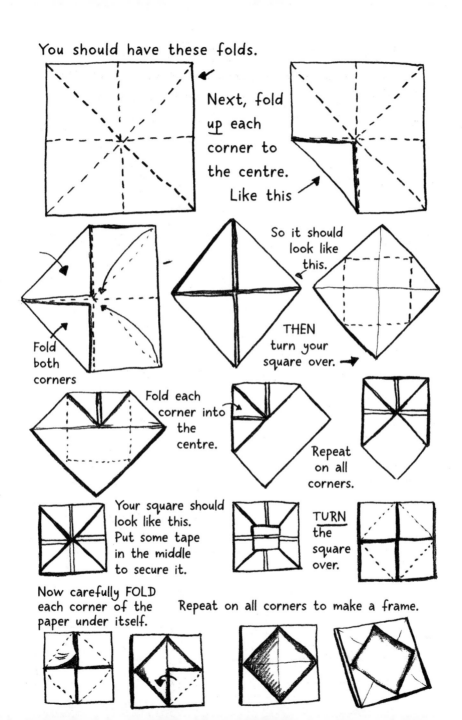

You should have these folds.

Next, fold up each corner to the centre. Like this

Fold both corners

So it should look like this.

THEN turn your square over. ➡

Fold each corner into the centre.

Repeat on all corners.

Your square should look like this. Put some tape in the middle to secure it.

TURN the square over.

Now carefully FOLD each corner of the paper under itself.

Repeat on all corners to make a frame.

Use the bit of paper you
cut off and fold it to
make a stand.

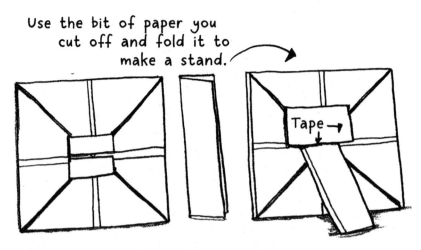

Tape →

Decorate the front of your frame.

Put your
picture here!

I've had an **excellent** day.

🙂 **M**um's impressed that I've kept myself
SO busy.

> I'm impressed.

"How was your day, Mum?"

I ask, being the nice son I am.

"It's been great, thanks.

But I did lose a very important contract
that I've been working on for a while.
I don't know what I did with it. I'm sure I had
it in my HAND when we came in,"

Mum tells me.

I keep quiet. I think I know what
happened to it.

> Whoops....

I make a **DISPLAY** of my photo frames and add some DRAWINGS, then I put them around the house for everyone to enjoy.

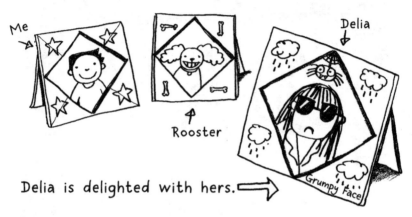

Me

Rooster

Delia

Grumpy Face

Delia is delighted with hers. ⇨

"It's nearly as good as that wool thing you made."

"You're welcome," I say.

"I can make you another one?" I offer.

"I'm good, thanks..." Delia says, waving me away.

(Her loss.)

I'm staying at home today as Dad's working in the shed. Mum's out and Delia's at college, which is GREAT news as I get the WHOLE house to myself.

I'm just settling in and making myself comfortable with the brand-NEW EXTRA-BIG cushions when Dad interrupts me.

"Tom! Come and play in the garden. It's such a nice sunny day – you don't want to be cooped up in here."

(I do.)

Dad holds open the door, letting me know it's not really a choice.

Sigh...

I follow Dad into his shed and spot a LOT
of stuff I haven't played with
for a long time.

"Dad, can you get these things out?" I ask.
(He doesn't seem keen.)

I hang around until he
eventually changes his mind.
Looks like the swing ball is
there too, and my
MONSTER hopper.

My MONSTER hopper has a few SLUGS on
it that need picking off before I
can have a GOOD BOUNCE.

Hello!

I bounce around the garden and past Dad's window a few times to show him how high I can go.

(It's more tiring than I remember.)

The great thing about SWING ball is that you can play it on your own, which is perfect for me today. I keep the ball moving for ages, then see how many times I can make it go round and round by HITTING it really hard.

Until the BALL FLIES off and hits the side of Dad's shed.

WHOOOSH!

Maybe you should do something else now?

Dad tells me.

"Awwww. Like what?" I ask.

"How about making a DEN or some kind of tent? You used to love doing that." (True.)

THIS is an EXCELLENT idea. ☺

I go into the front room and GRAB a nice selection of comfortable cushions to use as well

 as a few sheets and a blanket. All the kinds of things you need for a good DEN.

Pegs

I've got a great place to hide out while adding to my crisp packet collection and reading my **COMICS.** So far I'm enjoying half-term a lot.

As the SUN comes out, my den starts to HEAT up pretty fast.  I'm forced to open up the front and let in some air when I HEAR voices coming from next-door's garden.

> Look, Tom's made a fort.
> Do you think he's
> inside?

> Let's find out...

I'm listening to what they say when something bashes the side of my den!

A few pegs **PING** off and one of the sides slips down.

Hey! I say, crawling out.

AMY and June are looking over the fence at me and waving.

"You're there!" **AMY** says.

"Hi, Tom — I'm here for the holiday," June tells me.

"We wanted to see if you were inside,"
AMY explains.

"Well, here I am," I tell them both as I try to

FIX my den, but
it doesn't want
to stay up.

"So are you still in a band, then?"
June wants to know while I
struggle with a sheet.

Sigh...

"Yup – and **DUDE3** are still the best band **EVER,**" I add, wondering if she'll disagree.

"They're OK, I suppose," June replies. (This is a slight improvement on what she normally tells me.)

"Do you want to come over, Tom?" **AMY** asks me.

I don't answer straight away, as I'm enjoying having the **WHOLE** HOUSE and garden to myself with no one around to bother me.

We're making mini pizzas for lunch.

June adds.

"**OK!** I'll ask my dad," I say.

Dad takes me round so he can:

Quick

1) Check it's OK with June's dad

2) Have a very long CHAT about **Plastic Cup**

(The band June's dad is in.)

I get bored listening to them, so I go and find **AMY** and June.

"Hey, Tom – I was telling June how good at drawing you are," **AMY** says.

Thanks!

"Can you draw ... a **BASIN?**"

June wants to know, which is a bit ODD.

"Eeeeerrrrr, OK, I'll try," I say and have a go.

I do my best.

Basin

That's not a **BASIN!** June says.

"Yes it is," I tell her.

Bison are like BIG COWS with masses of HAIR.

"OH. I thought you said BASIN."

 "It's a good BASIN though, Tom."
AMY LAUGHS.

"What else can you draw?"
June asks.

"How about we all play a drawing game?"

I suggest.

 "Like this..." I draw Mr Fullerman
and a flower.

Then I turn the page over and ask AMY to
finish the drawings off.

"Oh, I remember how to play THIS! Don't look, Tom," she tells me. We do a few more drawings...

We swap drawings.

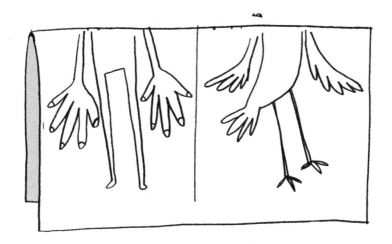

Then we open up all the drawings at the same time ...

... and they're EXCELLENT!

(In a slightly weird way.)

 After a few more drawings, I begin to drop hints about the pizzas.

"Good idea," **AMY** agrees.

"We can add our own toppings, then my dad will put them under the grill to cook," June tells us.

 "We're making them?" I ask.

"We are. Tom really likes tuna on pizza," **AMY** tells June.

"I hate tuna!" I say and pull a face while making noises too. Errrrrrrr Eeeeewwww

AMY and June start LAUGHING, so I do it some more. Then to REALLY make the point about tuna ...
I dramatically
((ROLL)) on the floor.

YUCK!

... just as June's dad comes in.

"You OK, Tom?" he asks me.

"Yes, I'm fine. Getting up now,"
I tell him awkwardly.

(No one makes me eat tuna and
the mini pizzas are ACE.)

How to Make a Mini Pizza

Take a pitta bread

Tomato puree

Cheese

Dried mixed herbs

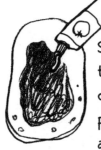 Spread the tomato puree on to the pitta bread in a thin layer.

Then add grated cheese on top.

Sprinkle a pinch of mixed herbs on top.

GET AN ADULT TO HELP WITH THIS BIT OF COOKING!

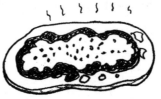 Put the mini pizza under the grill until the cheese melts.

Yum!
Be careful
– it will be
HOT!

You can add other things
to your pizza too:
    Peppers (chopped up)
    Onions
    Mushrooms
    Fresh herbs!
    Tuna (not for Tom!)

Yum!

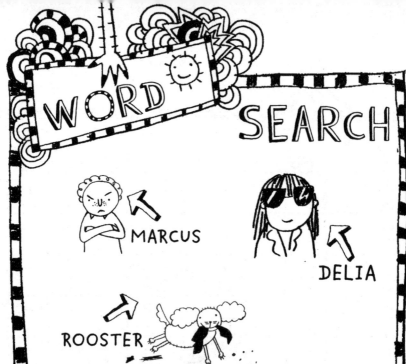

MARCUS

DELIA

ROOSTER

MONSTER

TOM

D	Y	P	W	K	J	U	R	S	D
F	R	O	O	S	T	E	R	D	O
S	E	P	J	B	O	I	A	E	G
F	A	P	M	A	A	C	N	L	Z
E	Y	T	O	M	P	B	T	I	O
I	W	R	N	D	D	S	A	A	M
S	O	M	S	A	R	M	G	L	B
H	D	I	T	G	G	T	E	D	I
A	Y	N	E	E	L	I	A	T	E
R	M	A	R	C	U	S	H	S	S

How to draw THIS MONSTER

Which line
leads to Amy?

Which line
leads to
June?

How to make a MONSTER PAPER CHAIN

You need – A4 paper   Glue stick   Pencil ← Pencil

Scissors ← Scissors

1) Take an A4 piece of paper and fold it in HALF.

2) Cut carefully along the fold.

3) Fold the paper in half to look like this.

Then fold it in half again ...

... and again ...

... fold

... and again ...

... fold

... and again ...

Your paper should look like THIS.

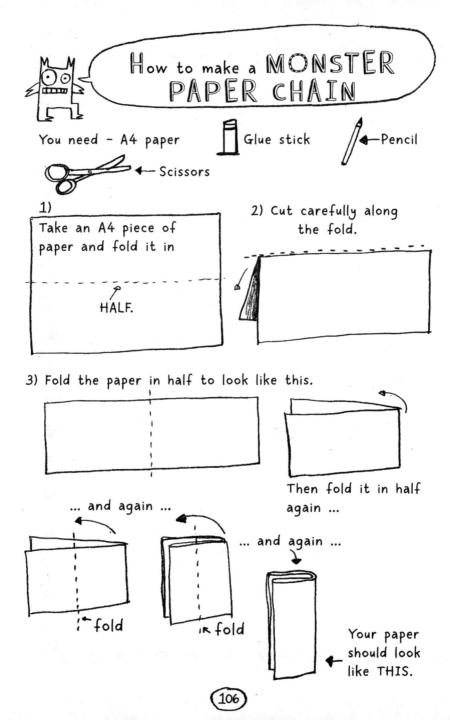

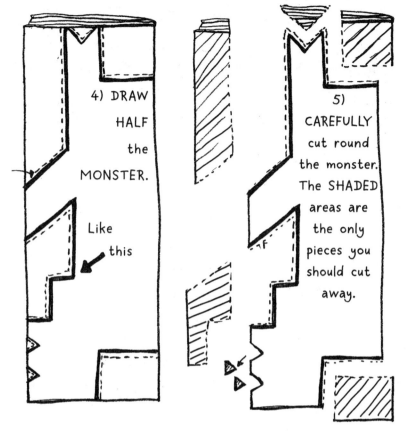

4) DRAW HALF the MONSTER.

Like this

5) CAREFULLY cut round the monster. The SHADED areas are the only pieces you should cut away.

6) Then OPEN your monster up and draw on its FACES.

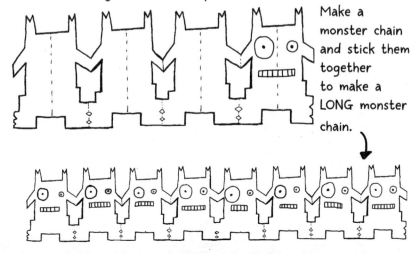

Make a monster chain and stick them together to make a LONG monster chain.

How to DRAW AMY

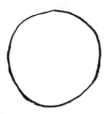

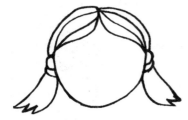

Space to doodle

I have a surprisingly  time with June and **AMY** and bring a spare pizza home so I can **IMPRESS** Mum and Dad with my cooking skills.

BYE

Pizza in foil

But when I get home, I eat it.

(I'll just TELL them how nice it was.)

(Empty plate)

Going next door made me forget all about the DEN the garden, which wouldn't have been a problem if it hadn't RAINED during the night.

A LOT.

In the morning, Dad says, "You brought
all the cushions back inside, didn't
you, Tom?"

 "EEErrrrmmm...
    I might have," I say quietly.

"They're still outside, aren't they?"
              Dad asks.

 "Yes, sorry - I was just trying to make
        a comfortable den," I have to admit.

"Let's go and get them quickly.
As long as you didn't use all the
BRAND-NEW BEST cushions..."
              Dad LAUGHS.

(I did...)

It says on the PLAN that I'm going to my cousins' house today.

So I have to be ALERT at all times because they often try and SURPRISE me, and not always in a good way. BOO!

They like playing TRICKS too, so I'm prepared for ANYTHING.

When Dad drops me at their house it's

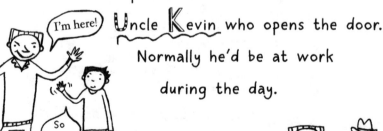

I'm here!

So am I...

Uncle Kevin who opens the door. Normally he'd be at work during the day.

"I pre-planned some days off to spend time with the boys over half-term," he says.

"Alice is at her ZUMBA class, in case you're wondering," he adds and does a little dance. The cousins tell him to stop.

"Thanks for having Tom round at such short notice. We got mixed up about half-term dates," Dad explains.

"Just as well someone in the family is organized!" Uncle Kevin says.

"But, Dad, you turned up a month early for parents' evening last week at school," the cousins remind him.

Uncle Kevin laughs. "It was a one-off. We'll see you later, Frank!" he tells Dad.

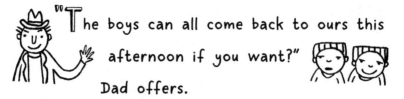

"The boys can all come back to ours this afternoon if you want?" Dad offers.

"We'll see – it's homework time in the afternoon, isn't it, boys?" Uncle Kevin says seriously.

"I've got **NO** homework at **ALL** for the ENTIRE holiday!"

I tell everyone happily.

"That's Oakfield School for you," Uncle Kevin says while shaking his head.

"Homework's **NOT** always the best way to learn," Dad points out, then smiles at me.

(I'm going to REMIND him about that – FOR EVER.)

Homework, Tom?

No need...

Sigh...

Homework? No thanks!

After Dad's gone, my stomach starts to rumble quite loudly.

"Did you have breakfast, Tom?" Uncle Kevin asks.

"Yes, but I'm happy to have MORE." I smile.

"LET'S MAKE TOAST!" the cousins shout out.

I agree. I like toast.

Uncle Kevin pulls a face when I start poking my finger into the bread.

"It's a TOAST DOODLE! See?" The cousins want to try them too now. Even Uncle Kevin has a go.

"I think Alice will like this," he says, then pops them under the grill.

But I'm not too sure.

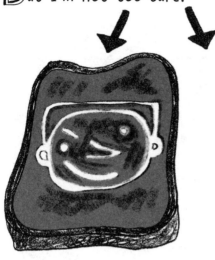

Ours look spectacular, though, and they taste great too...
The cousins like the one with my name on.

They make a few more of their own until Uncle Kevin tells them to stop.

That's enough, you two.

I think you should do something else for now,

he tells us.

So the cousins suggest we play cards...

Seeing their toast portraits gives me an idea for a card game we could play.

Playing SNAP with my cousins can be very STRESSFUL.

The SUSPENSE in between turning the cards over is TOO much and I keep shouting

SNAP!

too early and losing.

"Bad luck, Tom," the cousins say as I collect even MORE cards. "We like this game," they add.

(I can see why...)

After I LOSE another THREE games, I ask if they want to see my EXCELLENT card trick instead. Go on then...

they say.

 "OK, but you can't WATCH this bit. No looking!"

I have to say it a few times while I put the cards into

TWO PILEs.

(Granddad Bob showed me this trick.)

Then I wave my hands over the cards in what I hope is a very mysterious and

MAGICAL WAY.

I explain what the cousins have to do next. "Pick one card from this pile, LÒÓK at it and then put it back into the other pile anywhere you want. And don't tell me what it is."

The cousins are taking this VERY SERIOUSLY.

Once they're done, I shuffle the cards a LOT and do more magical hand waving. Then I spend a LONG time studying the cards carefully to find the ones they picked.

(I pull faces too.)

Finally, I take out two cards and say...

"These ARE YOUR CARDS!

Am I right?"

(I am.)

The cousins have **NO IDEA** how I did the
trick and want me to show them.

"A magician NEVER reveals their secrets,"
I tell them, which drives them **crazy.**

"We'll give you a caramel wafer,"
they say.

So I change my mind just as Aunty Alice
comes back from her ZUMBA class.

Her face is as RED as a tomato.

"Nice to see you, Tom. Are you all OK?"

We all say, "Yes!"

"GREAT – then you won't mind helping with a JOB?"
she adds sneakily.

(The word "JOB" doesn't sound promising.)

A job in my house is NORMALLY taking the bins out or tidying up.

But Aunty Alice wants us to decorate some CAKES!

"They're for the LEAFY GREEN OLD FOLKS' HOME charity cake stall. All they need is some icing and sprinkles. Can you do that for me?" she wants to know.

☆YES WE CAN!☆

This is my kind of JOB!

The cousins seem happy too. YEAH!

After we wash our hands, Aunty Alice gets out some icing and sprinkles and ALL the CAKES. ➡

"Where's Kevin? He was going to do this with you," she wonders.

 "He's on the phone ... again," the cousins say and Aunty Alice ROLLS her eyes.

"I'll show you what to do then," she says.

Aunty Alice does one cake with a spoonful of icing and tops it with sprinkles, then she wants us to do the rest.

"You carry on while I go and get changed."

But as soon as she leaves, the cousins both EAT A CAKE!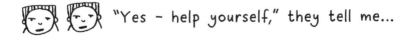

"Are we allowed?" I ask.

"Yes - help yourself," they tell me...

Aunty Alice `pops` her head back round the door...

"**Boys,** don't forget – these cakes are for charity. So **NO** eating them, OK?"

 "**OK,**" I answer.

The cousins still have their mouths full of cake, so they keep quiet until **A**unty **A**lice leaves.

They don't seem that bothered. "Mum won't notice – there are a lot of cakes on the plate."

"You should have one too, Tom," they add.

 I'm tempted.

"Maybe just ONE," I say and eat it quickly, before icing and putting sprinkles on the other cakes.

 I'm concentrating SO hard on what I'm doing that I don't notice what the cousins are up to.

It's only when I look up that I **SPOT** that even more

CAKES ARE MISSING!

 "Have you eaten more cakes?"

I ask.

(It's OBVIOUS they HAVE. The plate is
HALF EMPTY NOW!)

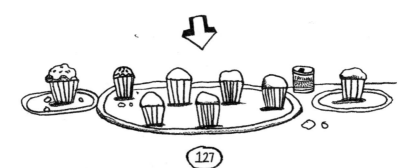

"**M**um won't mind. Besides, if she does, we won't get into trouble."

"Why's that?" I wonder.

  "We'll just say 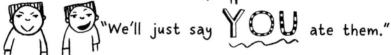 **YOU** ate them."

"WHAT?!"

  "You're a guest! She won't tell you off like she would us!"

The cousins LAUGH.

"Why should I take the blame? I didn't eat the cakes!" I remind them.

 "Yes, you did! You had a cake!" they say.

"I HAD ONE  CAKE. JUST ONE!"

I tell them firmly so they know it wasn't my fault! THEN I hear Aunty Alice coming back, and the cousins want me to "HIDE the PLATE!" so I stand right in front of it ...

when Aunty Alice walks in ...

... and her face is still **RE D.**

"How's the cake decorating going?

Have you nearly finished, boys?" she wants to know.

"Tom's got something to tell you,"

the cousins both say and start
LAUGHING!

"It wasn't me!" I let Аunty Аlice

know straight away.

"What wasn't, Tom?" she asks.

"The missing cakes!" I explain,

just as I **SPOT** that all the cakes

are BACK on the plate.

(130)

The cousins didn't eat them after all!
(I have to admit, they properly TRICKED me.)

"The cakes look great. Well done. Thanks for
helping out!" Aunty Alice tells us
and lets us eat a cake each.
(We keep quiet about the ones we already had.)

The cousins really want to know
how to do the card trick now.

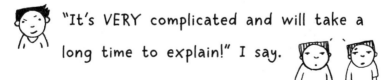

"It's VERY complicated and will take a
long time to explain!" I say.

How to do Granddad Bob's
EXCELLENT CARD TRICK

Take your pack of cards and when
no one is looking, sort them into
TWO PILES:

(Yes, it's THAT simple!)
Then offer ONE of the piles of cards to the
person (or people) you're playing the trick on.

Pick a card

✳ Don't let them SEE the cards are all ONE colour!

Now ask them to look at the card, REMEMBER it, and **PUT THE CARD BACK...**

IN THE OTHER PILE OF CARDS

Now you can SHUFFLE the cards and pretend to be trying to FIND their card. But REALLY ... it will BE EASY! It will be the ONLY RED card in the black cards.

Everyone will think you're

AMAZING

How to Make
SMALL SPONGE CAKES

You will need...

2 eggs

100g soft butter

100g self-raising flour

100g caster sugar

Large mixing bowl

Sieve

Paper cases

Bun tin

Wooden spoon

Teaspoons

Measure 100g of self-raising flour, then SIFT it into the mixing bowl.

Now add 100g of soft butter, 100g of caster sugar and break 2 eggs into the bowl.

Mix all the ingredients together with a wooden spoon until the mixture is smooth and creamy.

Now put your paper cake cases into your bun tin.

GET AN ADULT TO HELP WITH COOKING IN THE OVEN.

Set the oven to 180°C/350°F or Gas Mark 4 to warm up.

Put two teaspoons of cake mixture into the paper cases – don't overfill them.

Bake the cakes for about 20 minutes until golden brown, then put them on a cooling rack.

Get an adult to help you as they'll be HOT.

When your CAKES are cool,
decorate them with icing
sugar and sprinkles!

Or all kinds of different toppings,
like a cherry tomato.

(Joke...)

Yum...

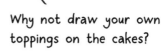
Why not draw your own
toppings on the cakes?

Here's another useful trick for doing your
NINE TIMES TABLE
On Your Fingers

Follow the pictures below.
Stretch out your fingers first (it helps).

◯ = Numbers in the circles show how many 9s.

△ = Numbers in the triangles show how many
fingers to hold <u>UP</u> on the <u>left</u> side.

☐ = Numbers in the squares show how many
fingers to hold <u>UP</u> on the <u>right</u> side.

Like this:

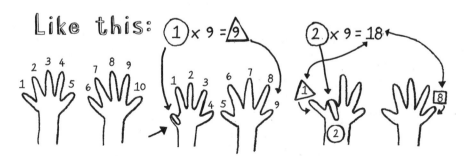

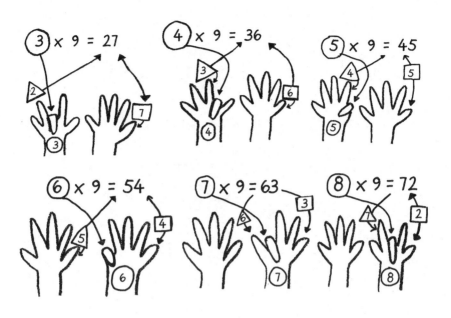

$9 \times 9 = 81$

$10 \times 9 = 90$

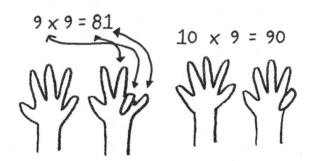

As you only have ten fingers the next two sums you have to remember.

$11 \times 9 = 99$

$12 \times 9 = 108$

How to make a
MONSTER ALIEN
SECRET MESSAGE

TOM GATES

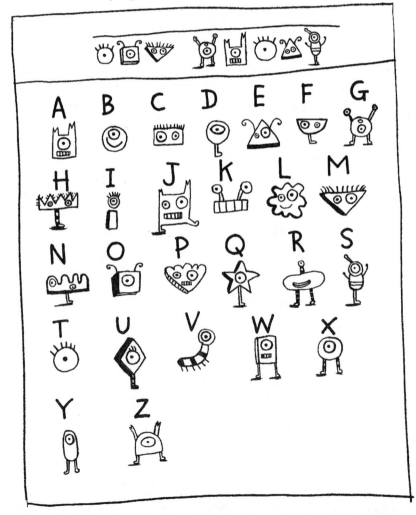

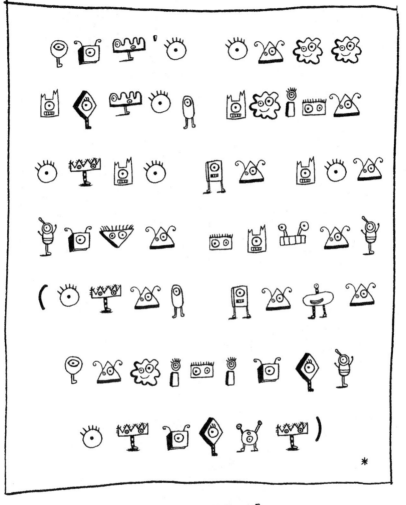

Ha! Ha!

TOAST doodles

Clean hands

Nice fresh bread

Take a slice of bread.
Press the bread down with your fingers
like this, making dents in the bread.

Then TOAST the bread.
(Make sure you get an adult to help!)
The TOAST will go brown, but stay white where you've pressed down.

TA-DA!
Yum.

NOW...

Doodle your own

Use these toasts
to doodle your
own designs.

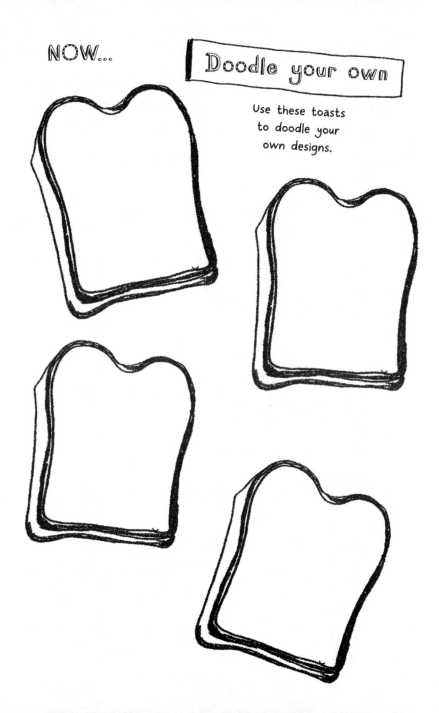

How to make a
FOIL SPIDER (Brilliant!)

Take a roll of FOIL and tear
or cut three strips off.
Be careful or ask an adult if
you're using scissors.

Fold one strip over and over
to make a thin but THICK leg.

You can
SCRUNCH
them as you go to make them rounder.
LIKE THIS

Now do the same with
the OTHER leg.

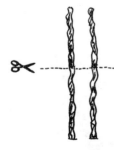

When you have two legs
together, cut them in the
middle so you have FOUR
legs the same length.

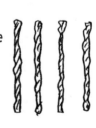

Put the legs on top of each other in a sort of STAR SHAPE. Then hold them in the centre and gently TWIST the legs together a little. This makes it easier to make the spider body.

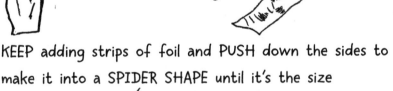

Once you've got your legs, use the other strip of foil to WRAP around the centre of the legs to make a body.

KEEP adding strips of foil and PUSH down the sides to make it into a SPIDER SHAPE until it's the size you want. Then gently bend the legs up into a SPIDER SHAPE.

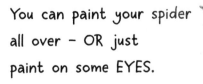

Like this

You can paint your spider all over – OR just paint on some EYES.

Draw your own spider

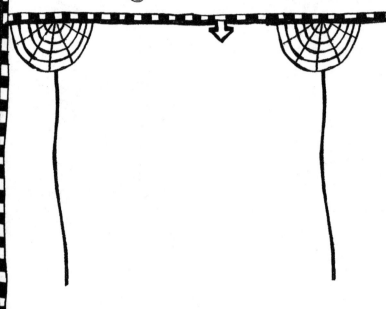

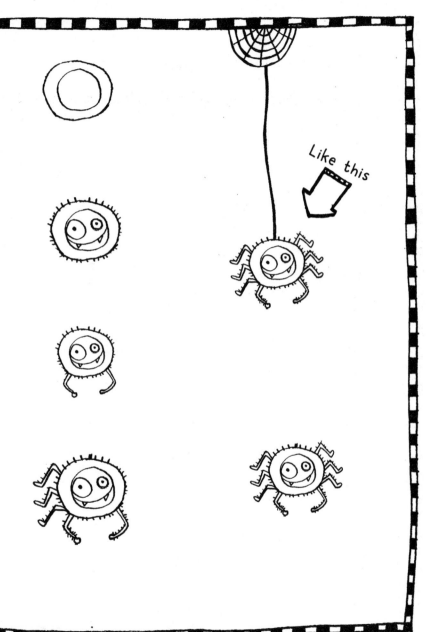

Like this

I keep the cousins guessing for as long as I can before I show them.

Ha! Ha!

DAY FOUR

Mum's at work,  Dad's too busy
and Delia's at college, so **THE FOSSILS**
are coming over later. I'm looking forward to
Derek  coming back tomorrow as well.
We'll be able to catch up and maybe have a band
practice too.

I can do ANYTHING I

want today because I HAVE

NO HOMEWORK
AT ALL!

Sigh...

But I can't decide what to do first.

"I'll make toast, then run around the garden," I say to myself, as that sounds like a good idea. I try and break my ALL-TIME record of THREE times round the garden before the toast **POPS UP.** But I get distracted by an ants' nest and watch that for a while.

Wow, ants!

I miss my record, but I get to eat my toast anyway.

As I'm relaxing on the sofa (with my toast), THE FOSSILS arrive and they're BOTH holding up T-shirts and WAVING them around like flags.

Cooee!

"HELLO, TOM! Look what we've brought! Now ... guess what we want you to do with them?" they ask me.

"EEEEEEEErrrrrrr ... wear them?"

Chocolate spread

"We want you to help us doodle on them! We're going to wear them at the charity cake sale. There's one for you too," Granny tells me.

"Great!" I say and go to find my special fabric pens to draw with.

My grandparents do a lot of nice things at LEAFY GREEN OLD FOLKS' HOME.

They've organized events like:

BINGO nights

Discos

Quiz nights

Team Sprightly

Comedy evenings

Pottery painting

Biscuit Decorating

DOGZOMBIES played their first-ever

gig there, too.

(Thanks, Fossils!)

Spending time with my grandparents is

always good *FUN*, AND I get to ask them

QUESTIONS and find out lots of things

I didn't know.

As I'm showing them HOW to doodle on their T-shirts, Granddad tells me that MY dad and Uncle Kevin once made a BIG mess in the house with **PAINT** and THEN blamed it on a **GHOST!**

I can imagine them doing that.

Here are some other interesting **FACTS** I found out while doodling:

Dad and Uncle Kevin were in a punk band together a very LONG time ago.

They used to jump up and down a lot.

Really?

Granny Mavis has driven a BIG lorry AND she can plough a field.

Really?

It's true!

Granddad has got a tattoo!

A bird!

Then, as we're doing our T-shirts, Granny tells us a story. When she was younger she once had dinner with a VERY FAMOUS singer.

 "Did you?" I ask.

THIS is news to Granddad too.

"I've never heard about that before!" he says.

"You never asked!" Granny laughs. I have a photo of us somewhere...

"WHO WAS IT, THEN?" I want to know.

> **LOOK** at my **MARVELLOUS** T-shirt! This is going to look FANTASTIC at the **CAKE** sale!

Granny says (skilfully changing the subject). Then she reminds Granddad that his T-shirt was supposed to have a **CAKE** on it. So he makes a little change.

> There you go!

CAKE Rock Star

We finish our doodling just as Delia comes back from college, so I show her my new T-shirt.

"That's amazing," she says, not very convinced.

"You're all such a talented family," Granny Mavis says.

I offer to do a T-shirt for Delia too.

"I'm on holiday – I have a lot of time." But she doesn't seem to hear me, which is a shame.

Doodle anything you like

GRANNY MAVIS'S FISH BISCUIT RECIPE

Get an adult to help you with the HOT STUFF (oven), and the SHARP STUFF (knife).
(No accidents please!)

Ingredients

Wash your hands PLEASE!

125g softened butter

Caster Sugar

50g caster sugar

Plain Flour

175g plain flour

sieve

spoon

rolling pin

mixing bowl

Greaseproof paper

Plus white icing sugar and raisins (for the eyes)

1 Pre-heat the oven to 180°c/350°f – gas mark 4.

2 Weigh out the plain flour and sieve into a bowl – then add the caster sugar.

3 Add the 125g of butter, then gently rub all the ingredients together until it looks like breadcrumbs.

4 Mix the dough into a ball shape. (Add a tiny bit of milk if it needs it.)

5 Gently roll out the mixture. Dust the surface and rolling pin with flour to stop it from sticking.

6 Carefully cut out a fish shape from the dough and place on the greaseproof paper on the tin.

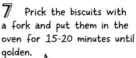

7 Prick the biscuits with a fork and put them in the oven for 15-20 minutes until golden.

8 Then get an adult to help you take them out when cooked.

Allow them to cool on a rack. Then to make the EYES you can use a BLOB of icing and a raisin.

        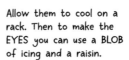

Try making your own FISH biscuits
and drawing them here.

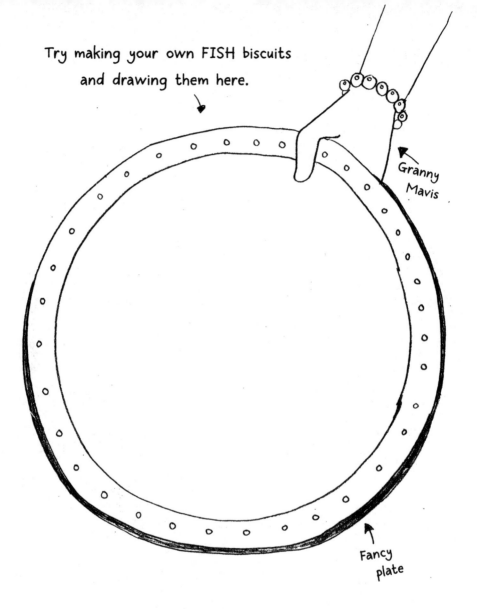

Granny
Mavis

Fancy
plate

This plate is for doodling on.

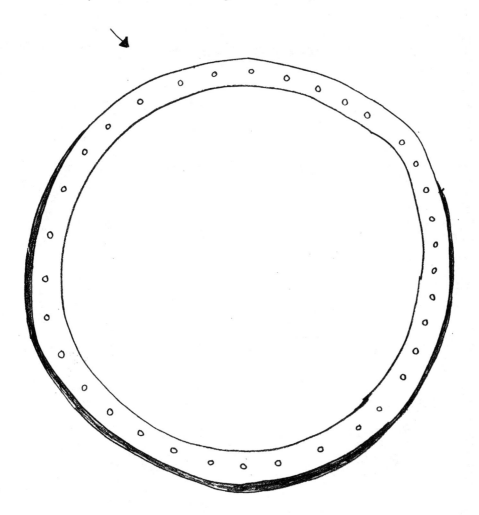

IMAGINE what other SNACKS and flavours there could be!

What's in the bowl?

Crispy star and cheese nibbles

Spicy alien?

Salt and onion shells

Chocolate-covered worms with sprinkles

YUM

Sausage and SOCK flavour

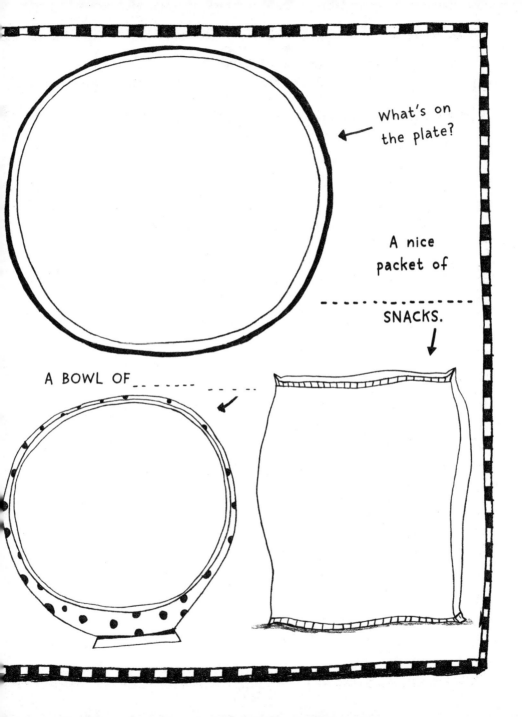

What's on the plate?

A nice packet of

SNACKS.

A BOWL OF

How to play ★BINGO★ (or biscuit bingo)

B	I	N	G	O

Empty bingo card

You can play BINGO with any number of players. One person needs to be the CALLER.
Copy the bingo cards to make your own.

Each player has their OWN card. Add the word BINGO and fill in the squares with any numbers between 1 and 50. I've added some biscuits too...

B	I	N	G	O
4	8	29	20	2
50	🍪	9	1	40
3	12	30	7	▭

B	I	N	G	O

Don't repeat any numbers, though!

NEXT: Write the numbers from 1 to 50 on a piece of paper like in the picture. ⟍1⟍ Then cut them out and fold ↴ each number up so you can't see the number.

Do the same for all of them (including the biscuits).

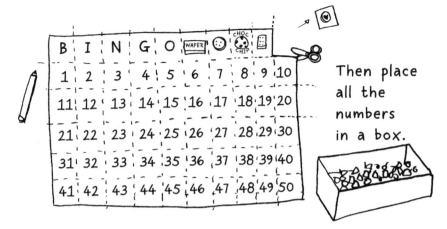

Then place
all the
numbers
in a box.

When all the players have their cards ready, the caller begins by taking one number and calling it out.

BINGO!

The bingo players check their cards and put a <u>cross</u> over any numbers (or biscuits!) they have. The <u>winner</u> is the person who has a full card <u>first</u>.

Design your own T-shirt

My T-shirt for Delia

Is THAT Granny Mavis?

Bugs reading

DAY FIVE

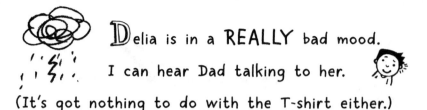 Delia is in a REALLY bad mood.

I can hear Dad talking to her.

(It's got nothing to do with the T-shirt either.)

"All you have to do is keep an eye on Tom for two hours. It's not much to ask, Delia!" Dad says.

I don't like the idea of DELIA being in charge.

"Why do I have to look after Tom? It's my ONLY morning free. I'm at college the rest of the time! I have plans," Delia complains.

"We ALL have plans, Delia. Sometimes you just have to CHANGE those plans," Dad says.

 "I'm FINE! Delia doesn't have to stay with me," I offer helpfully.

"Sorry, Tom," Dad tells me, so neither of us has a choice,

which makes Delia even

GRUMPIER. ⟹

I'm not happy either, so I go and find Mum.

"You've been **really** good this week, Tom – apart from ruining the cushions. I PROMISE we'll do something lovely as a family this weekend," Mum explains and that cheers me UP. I'm in such a good mood.

 I even ask Delia is she wants to watch TV with me.

She doesn't.

Then Dad steps in and makes a suggestion.

"Why don't I drive you both to the library? There's always **LOTS** of things going on. You can bring back your books as well, Tom."

It's a GREAT idea!

Even Delia doesn't seem to mind about this ... until she sees all the books I have to bring back.

"Oh, for goodness' sake! How many have you got?"

"I like taking out the BIG books about insects and creepy-crawlies," I tell her, which makes her **SHUDDER.**

"**R**ight, come on, you two – let's go," Dad says, trying to be **jolly**.

Delia is still not smiling. In the car she even tells me to stop talking, which is a bit RUDE.

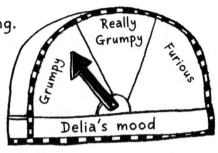

Really Grumpy

Grumpy

Furious

Delia's mood

When we get to the library, Dad tells us, "I'll pick you up in an hour – unless you want to stay longer?"

"We won't," Delia replies quickly.

I follow her inside and hope she cheers up a bit.

Hurry up.

"At least it will be QUIET in the library – I'll get some peace and won't have to listen to any NOISE," Delia mumbles.

But THAT'S not going to happen.
The library is FULL of children having *FUN* and
being lively.

"It's the holidays – what did you expect?"
I point out to Delia.

"Well, I'm going over THERE to the
QUIET ZONE. You can go to the kids'
section. Stay where I can see you.
OK, Tom?"

 "OK," I tell her.

(Delia is being super BOSSY!)

I drop off my books then decide to check out
the /NEW BOOKS\ shelf. I spot one that
I REALLY want to read!  YES!

It's only **THE BOOK OF MISERABLE MONSTERS.**

This is **FANTASTIC**!
I rush over to get it from the shelf ...

... when SOMEONE ELSE
GRABs IT from the
OTHER SIDE!

NO!

I say, because I recognize the
FACE smiling back at me through the shelves.

NEW BOOKS

MONSTER

UNICORN TRICKS

It's Marcus Meldrew, and he's smirking at me
while HOLDING THE BOOK!

"I was just about to take that out!"

"**W**ell, you'll just have to wait until I bring it back ... much later," he says.

(Marcus is being SUPER annoying.)

 A nice librarian asks me if I need any help as she's seen I've missed out. She recommends a few other books, then says, "Let me see when the monster book is due back."

Which is nice of her.

I go over to the oversized-book section and try to ignore Marcus, who's already reading the **MONSTER BOOK.** He keeps LOOKING at me and

LAUGHING.

"This book is SO GOOD!" he tells me.

"Really..." I sigh.

Ha! Ha! Ha!

"Yes, it is," he adds.

I find an **extra**-large insect book and decide to read about ants.  This keeps me busy for a while and takes my mind off Marcus, who's still LAUGHING a little TOO loudly for my liking!

Ha! Ha! Ha! Ha! Ha!

This is SO FUNNY!

Ha!

Ha! Ha! Ha!

(It's not easy blocking out his noise...)

But when I see a kid put a CRAZY FRUIT BUNCH book BACK on the return shelf, I know that book is for ME!

I am determined

to get there

FIRST...

I stand up

and do

some extra

fast walking

when I SPOT

Marcus is

<u>running.</u>

So I go

faster

and faster.

I'm

nearly

there...

Crazy
Fruit Bunch

Delia comes over and tells me:

1)   to stop jumping up and down,

2)   that she's ready to go.

I wave BYE to Marcus because NOW I have

the CRAZY FRUIT BUNCH book I

don't mind about NOT getting

the **MONSTER BOOK.**

Marcus doesn't wave back.

As we're waiting for Dad to pick us up, I notice
that Delia has taken some books out too.

 "What are you reading?" I ask.

"Never you mind," she says.

"Why don't you want to tell me?" I wonder.

"It's for a project and it's none of your business,"

Delia tells me.

 Which is odd, because I think it is my business.

I have to wait for Delia to put the books in her room and go out before I get the chance to take a *SNEAKY PEEK* at what she's got.

And NONE of her books are what I expected. Who knew?

Join the Dots

Draw Marcus and fill in the speech bubbles.

He could be thinking something really SMART (not).

How to draw Marcus Meldrew

How to Make a Comic Folder

You will need: THREE pages of a comic to make a big folder

Enough sticky-back plastic to cover all three pages front and back (S.B.P. = sticky back plastic).

Ribbon or string

Some scissors

Comic

Peel back the paper from the S.B.P.

Get an adult to help as S.B.P. can be tricky! Make sure you have a clean surface too. (No biscuit crumbs!)

Cut SIX pieces of sticky-back plastic – slightly larger than your comic pages

Carefully place your comic page on top of the S.B.P. Start at one end and GENTLY rub the comic as you go.

Comic

Sticky side up

Turn the comic over and fold down the edges.

Repeat with ALL three pages.

Then trim the corners OFF like this. ➤

Comic

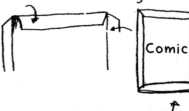

Comic

So each page looks like this.

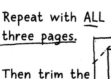

Then do the same thing with the other side of the comic page.

Comic | Comic front

You should have THREE fully covered pages at the end.
Now it's time to stick them together.

Choose which page you want for the front. Then cut a strip

of S.B.P. and stick <u>two</u> pages together. Trim off the edges or fold them over.

To make the pocket <u>inside</u>, fold the last page in half.

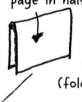

Place on the inside right (folded EDGE up).

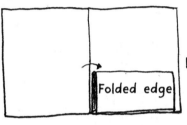

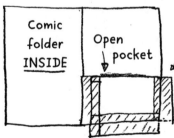

Folded edge

Then cut <u>MORE</u> strips of S.B.P. to stick the pocket in place.

Comic folder <u>INSIDE</u>

Open pocket

Fold over S.B.P. to make it look neater and stick the pocket in place. It should look like THIS.
Should fit a pie<u>ce</u> of paper.

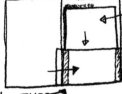

To finish off, close the folder and PUNCH a hole in the middle. Then thread your ribbon or string through to HOLD it together.

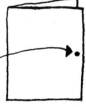

ONE COMIC FOLDER!

Doodle
your own
book marker.

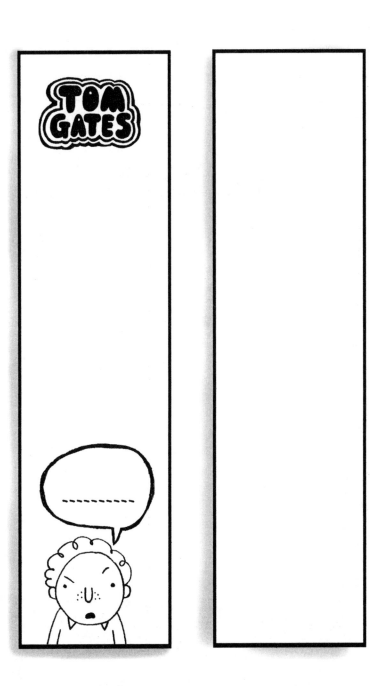

LOOK! DOODLE your OWN book cover!

Doodle here

Something to **KEEP OUT** incredibly ANNOYING OLDER SISTERS (or BROTHERS!) (or FAMILY!)

KEEP OUT!
(Especially DELIA)

CUT around the edge and hang on the handle of your door. Get an adult to help.

DAY SIX

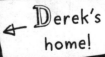

Hooray! **D**erek's home and holding up a sign at his window.

Shall I
come
over?

YES!
Bring
Rooster!

OK!
☺

Today is all sorted then.

Delia's gone over to Avril's and taken her books, which is GOOD NEWS as she wouldn't be happy that Rooster is spreading his fur everywhere. Now she'll never know.

When Derek arrives I open the door and Rooster goes CRAZY and disappears upstairs into what sounds like Delia's bedroom!

 "Uh-oh... We'd better go get him," Derek says.

"Don't panic, Delia's gone out. Rooster is fine!" I say. Then Derek and I have a CHAT about what we've both been doing during the holiday. I'm about to tell him about AMY and June, only Delia comes back and gives us a SHOCK.

"WHAT ARE YOU DOING HERE?" I shout.

"I live here... I've forgotten my bag," she says and goes into the kitchen.

WE DON'T HAVE MUCH TIME TO FIND ROOSTER.

"I hope he's NOT still in Delia's room..." Derek says, so we run upstairs to check before Delia follows us.

Rooster! Rooster! *Rooster!* we keep calling.

I don't think he's there.

Next, we check in my room, but Rooster seems to have DISAPPEARED!

Where?

"He's GOT to be here somewhere!" I say as Delia starts walking up the stairs.

She's already *SNEEZING!*

ATCHOO!

Uh-oh...

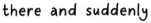"**W**e'll be in TROUBLE if Rooster is there and suddenly **LEAPS OUT** at Delia!" **D**erek says.

All we can do is keep quiet and LISTEN out for Delia shouting.

Then **D**erek spots that Rooster is outside in the GARDEN. So we rush downstairs to pick Rooster up and keep him away from Delia.

We all hide behind the sofa until Delia leaves the house and it's SAFE to come out.

Delia is still *SNEEZING!*

as she slams the front door.

Phew...

We all breathe a sigh of relief.

(Even Rooster.)

This seems like a good time to watch some TV.

Especially as

is on!

It's an excellent idea.

Derek and I are having such a good laugh that
we don't see what Rooster is doing ...

... until it's too late.

"Rooster, n⊙t the cushions!"

Another cushion that's been

RuInEd!

Oh, no...

Trying to think of EXCUSES to cover up for
Rooster would have been a lot EASIER to do ...
if ONLY he hadn't ripped

Delia's pillow

nibbled Mum and

Dad's socks

and chewed up my

pants as well.

No wonder
Rooster is tired.

Doodle here

How to draw my
GRUMPY SISTER DELIA

Draw this
shape.

Then her
glasses...

Colour
them in.

Ears ... (even though she doesn't LISTEN)

Add her manky hair ....

... and add a gloom cloud.

How to draw a
DOGZOMBIE in stages.

How to play
MONSTER BATTLESHIPS

It's like **normal** battleships only with

MONSTERS instead.

Here's how we play it:

There's a KING monster – worth [20] points.

And a QUEEN monster – worth another [20] points.

Then there are five mini monsters – worth [5] points each.

And five BLOB monsters, each worth [1] point.

You each draw a square and number them. Then draw all your monsters in different squares, like this.

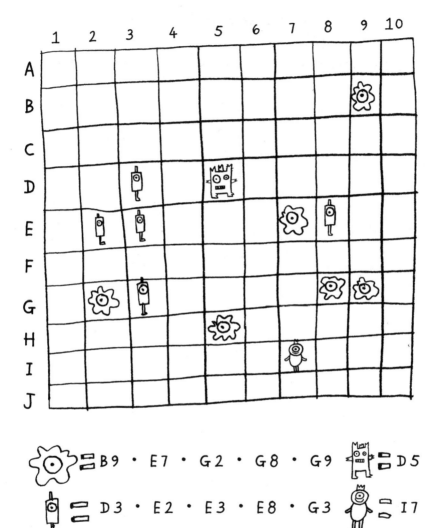

Then try to guess where each other's monsters are!

Make a stand-up MONSTER

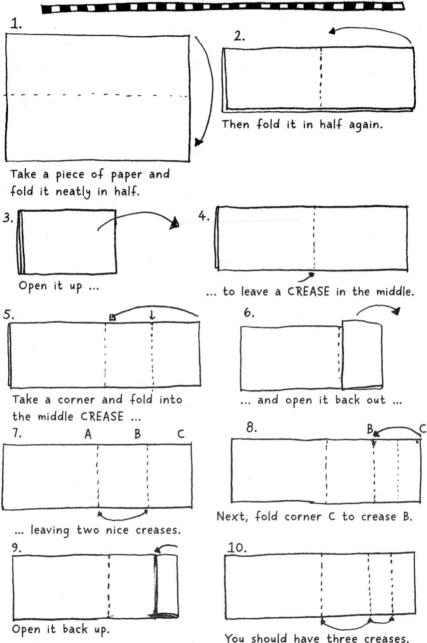

1. Take a piece of paper and fold it neatly in half.

2. Then fold it in half again.

3. Open it up ...

4. ... to leave a CREASE in the middle.

5. Take a corner and fold into the middle CREASE ...

6. ... and open it back out ...

7. A   B   C
... leaving two nice creases.

8. B   C
Next, fold corner C to crease B.

9. Open it back up.

10. You should have three creases.

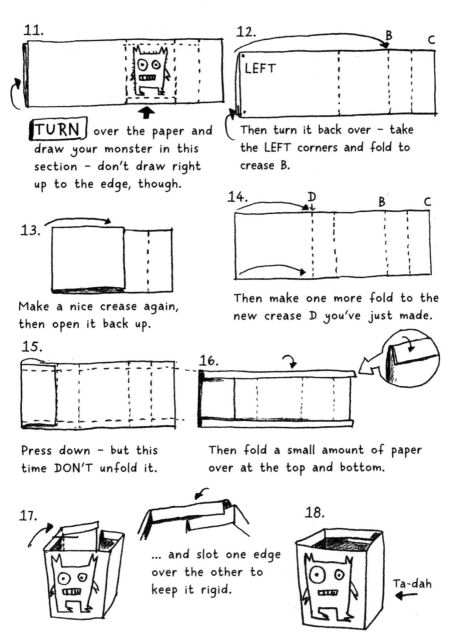

11. TURN over the paper and draw your monster in this section – don't draw right up to the edge, though.

12. LEFT
Then turn it back over – take the LEFT corners and fold to crease B.

13. Make a nice crease again, then open it back up.

14. D B C
Then make one more fold to the new crease D you've just made.

15. Press down – but this time DON'T unfold it.

16. Then fold a small amount of paper over at the top and bottom.

... and slot one edge over the other to keep it rigid.

17. FOLD the monster to look like the picture ...

18. Ta-dah
It should look like this!

LOOK!

Make your monsters into a GAME.

Add numbers to them and use a scrunched-up

piece of paper as a ball to knock them over

with (like skittles).

The WINNER is the one with the most

POINTS!

RESULT!

DAY SEVEN

It's my LAST DAY OF THE HOLIDAY and Dad suggests we should have a picnic.

"Brilliant!" I say, as I LOVE picnics. Delia doesn't want to come because she's still CROSS about Rooster being in her room and chewing her pillow. "WHY did you let him in there?" she asks, like I had a CHOICE!

Mum thinks a picnic sounds like a good idea too, but it takes SUCH A LONG TIME to:

1) Get the food together,

2) Decide where to go,

3) Pack my bag,

That the whole SKY has turned a really DARK SHADE OF GREY...

... and it looks like it's going to pour with rain.

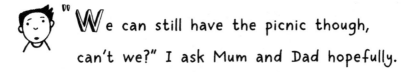"We can still have the picnic though,
can't we?" I ask Mum and Dad hopefully.

"You know what will happen. As SOON as
we leave, there'll be a STORM!" Mum says,
looking at the sky.

"Should we RISK it?" Dad wonders.

"Yes!" I say.

"Let's give it ten minutes – it might clear up,"
Mum says.

So we all wait ... and it gets darker, but
doesn't quite rain.

But Mum and Dad don't think we should go.

"It's not **POURING** yet."

I try and get them to change their minds.

They can see I'm disappointed, so Dad makes

another suggestion.

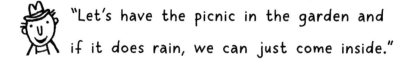

"Let's have the picnic in the garden and

if it does rain, we can just come inside."

"That's perfect!" Mum agrees.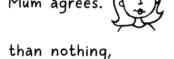

It's better than nothing,

so I say,  OK.

$\mathbb{I}$ take out a blanket and a couple of cushions

and put them down by the tree.

um and Dad bring out the food and we set it all out (sandwiches, scones 🍰 , JAM, drinks, salad stuff for them.) It's a FEAST!

"This is nice, isn't it? <u>Lots</u> of fresh air – we can pretend we're in a FOREST," Dad says, looking around.

Mum spots the swing ball is still out and CHALLENGES me to a game. "I used to be good at this!" Mum tells me while missing the ball (more than once).

(This time I remember <u>not</u> to hit it too hard.)

We have a few games, then I SIT back on the blanket, and that's when I notice ...

ALL THE ANTS!

THEY are

EVERYWHERE!

(And in the food, too.)

It wasn't the RAIN that forced us to abandon
our picnic after all. (At least I won at swing
ball, though.)

How to Make a Paper Aeroplane

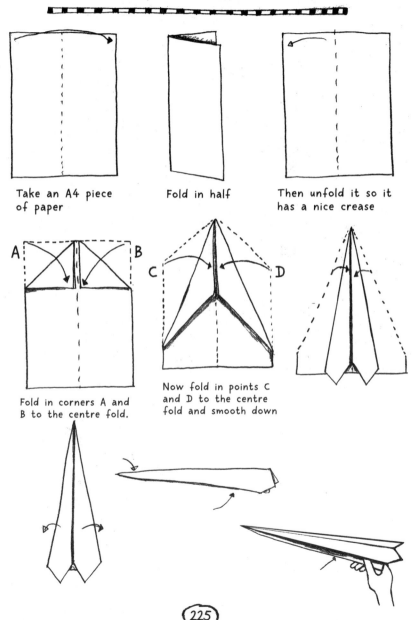

Take an A4 piece of paper

Fold in half

Then unfold it so it has a nice crease

Fold in corners A and B to the centre fold.

Now fold in points C and D to the centre fold and smooth down

How to make a KITE

You'll need:

A bin bag or Plastic bag

String

Scissors

Sticky tape

Two wooden sticks, one longer than the other (you could use garden sticks)

Pen

Ruler

(You might need a bit of adult help with this)

Use a single-sheet plastic bag or bin liner for the kite. Spread it out like this. →

The shorter stick goes over the longer one. Tie them together with string like in the picture. NICE AND TIGHTLY.

Put the sticks on the plastic and use the ruler to mark out a diamond shape larger than the sticks with the pen.

larger than the sticks

Cut out the diamond shape and keep the corners.

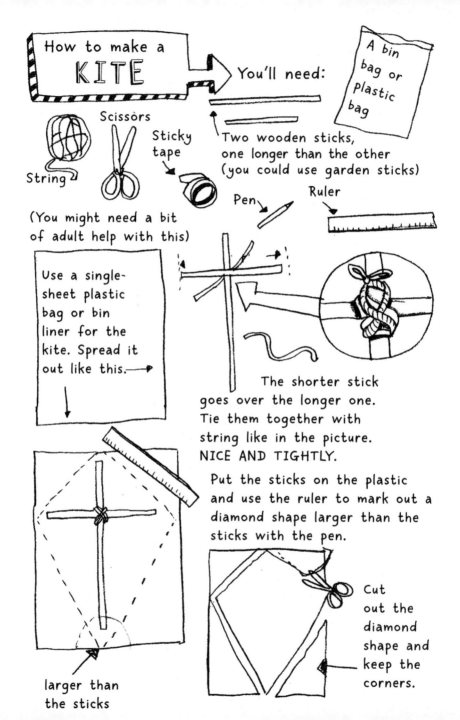

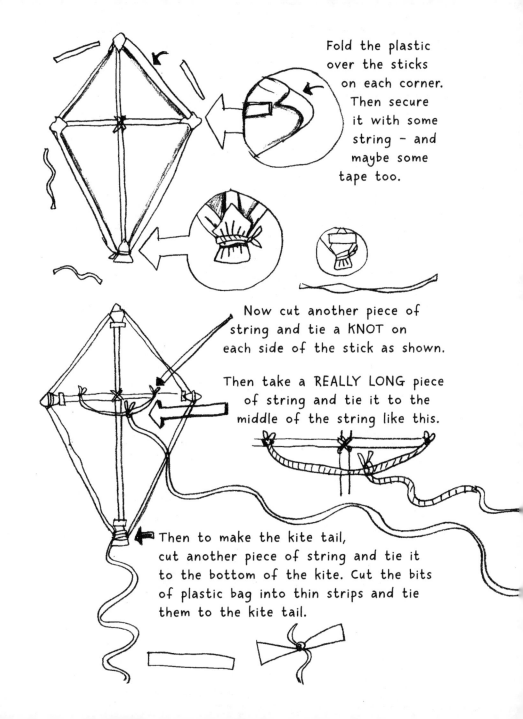

Fold the plastic over the sticks on each corner. Then secure it with some string – and maybe some tape too.

Now cut another piece of string and tie a KNOT on each side of the stick as shown.

Then take a REALLY LONG piece of string and tie it to the middle of the string like this.

Then to make the kite tail, cut another piece of string and tie it to the bottom of the kite. Cut the bits of plastic bag into thin strips and tie them to the kite tail.

Add your own ants

How to make and play SKITTLES with plastic bottles (Good for rainy days)

Take some empty plastic bottles that are roughly the same size. Check the lids FIT nicely (get a grown-up to help if you need to). Then fill them with enough water so they're STURDY, but not too tricky to knock down.

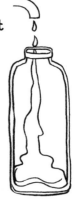

You can use a STICKY NOTE or paper and sticky tape to add NUMBERS on to the bottles. These are POINTS SCORED when the bottles are knocked down.

Use a scrunched-up ball of FOIL as a ball
– or something soft
if you're playing inside.

You can use some bottles with no water to
make them easier to knock down.

Decide how far away to stand and put down
a MARKER of some kind so everyone stands
the same distance away.

Then PLAY!

Yes!

Knocking all the bottles down is a

STRIKE

and is very impressive.

Doodle anything you like:

My holiday has gone

SO FAST and

I'm still in "staying in bed" mode when Delia
knocks on my door (loudly!) and says,

"GET UP, TOM!
You know you've got school TODAY!"

Have I?
Yes, I have!

"I'm already up!" I say, even though I'm not.
(I can tell Delia is enjoying waking me up.) I get
dressed as quickly as I can, but I keep finding
ANTS in my SHOES and SOCKS!

They're hard to SHAKE off.

I rush downstairs and can see

Mum's already left for work.

Dad offers to drive me to

school while Delia enjoys watching me panic.

I grab all my stuff  and go outside.

It looks like Derek has already left, so I jump

in the car.

When we pull up outside, there's no one about –

school must have already started.

"BYE, DAD!" I shout as I

jump out of the car.

"Don't RUN, Tom!"

Dad calls after me.

"I haven't forgotten anything!"

I shout back ...

... only I have.

I forgot it's INSET day.

(There's a big sign at the door.)

At least I'm not the **ONLY** kid who's forgotten. He's trying to hide from me, but I can see Marcus is here too.

Ha!
    Ha!
        Ha!

Keep your BEADY EYES open for the other hilarious TOM GATES books!

For more news about Liz Pichon and the Tom Gates books, go to: Lizpichon.com
AND to Scholastic's fantastic Tom Gates website: www.scholastic.co.uk/tomgatesworld

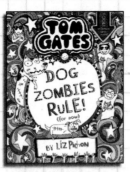

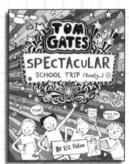

So many books

ONE VILE VILLAIN.
TWO VICIOUS DOGS.
THREE COURAGEOUS CHILDREN.

The flying shoes of your most EPIC dreams.
WELCOME TO SHOE TOWN.

Meet Ruby, Bear and Chelsea.
They're RUNNING out of time to
RESCUE their inventor dad from his
HIDEOUS boss, WENDY WEDGE.

She'll do anything to win the glitzy GOLDEN SHOE AWARD
and knows that entering flying shoes is her hot
ticket to the trophy. Flying shoes that Ruby
and Bear just HAPPEN to be hiding...

This can only mean one thing... it's SHOE WARS!

A laugh-out-loud, gadget-packed,
wedge-of-your-feet adventure like no other!

A *Sunday Times* children's book of the year.

"Full of Pichon's characteristic warmth, humour
and quirky illustrations" *The Bookseller*

Liz Pichon is one of the UK's best-loved and bestselling creators of children's books.

Her TOM GATES series has been translated into 45 languages, sold millions of copies worldwide, and has won the Roald Dahl Funny Prize, the Blue Peter Book Award for Best Story and the younger fiction category of the Waterstones Children's Book Prize.

In the ten years since THE BRILLIANT WORLD OF TOM GATES first published, the books have inspired the nation's children to get creative, whether that's through reading, drawing, doodling, writing, making, music or performing.

"I wanted to FILL the books with ALL the things I loved doing when I was a kid. It's just the best feeling ever to know children are enjoying reading the books, because I love making them. So thank you so much for choosing Tom Gates and keep reading and doodling!"

OUT NOW

DON'T GET BORED, GET BUSY!

The must-have activity book for fans
of Tom Gates. Packed with doodle ideas,
fun games, brilliant puzzles and perfect
pranks to play on older siblings – there's
hours of fun ahead.

Tom Gates is TREMENDOUS
and so are his TALES!

The absolutely brilliant, extra special new bestseller from multi-million copy selling author and illustrator Liz Pichon.

TREMENDOUS!

POSTCARD

THE ADDRESS TO BE WRITTEN ON THIS SIDE

10 YEARS

Thank you all so much if you took
part in the doodle competition.
It was so hard to choose a winner –
they were all brilliant.
WELL DONE!

Daisy, 8, Peterborough

Ava, 9, London

Oscar, 8, Todmorden

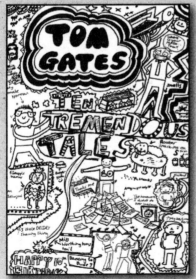

Laila, 14, London

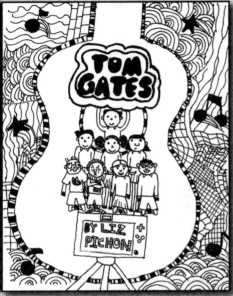

Theo, 8, Gloucestershire

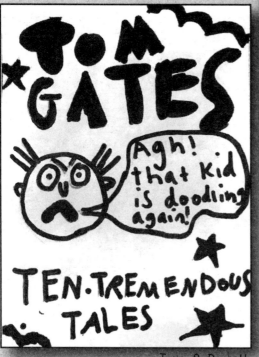

Josie, 8, Penarth

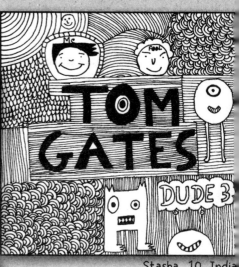

Stasha, 10, India

Ayaan, 9, Bromley

Ayaan, 9, Bromley

Emilia, 6, London

Iyla, 7, Eastbourne

Alexa, 10, Loughborough

Euan, 11, Stockport

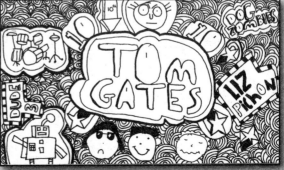

River, 10, Falmouth

Annalie, 10, Woking

Lilly, 8, Eastbourne

Cayden, 11, Ferndale, Rhondda Cynon Taf

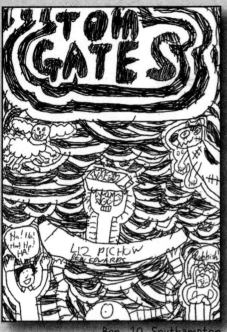
Ben, 10, Southampton

Jess, 12, Derbyshire

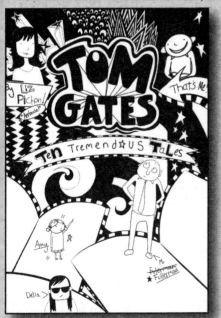
Inari, 13, Surrey

Wren, 6, Lancaster

Sebastian, 8, Telford

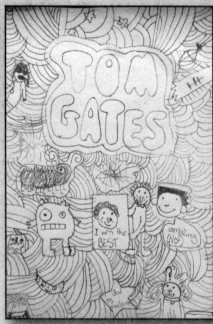
Isla, 9, Silverstone

Thomas, 8, Liverpool

Luca, 8, Eastbourne

Aurora, 10, Surrey

Camille, 9, Kent

Luca, 8, Eastbourne

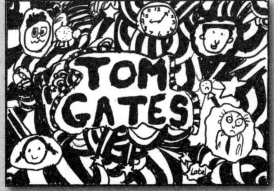
Annie, 7, Shropshire

Sidra, 11, London

Harrison, 6, Hertfordshire

Evie, 12, Stockport

Joshua, 9, Middlesbrough

Oenone, 12, Bedfordshire

Ralph, 8, Chichester

Joseph, 9, Stockport

Zackaria, 8, Edinburgh

Ruari, 10, London

Joseph, 9, Tonbridge

Leo, 7, Bristol

Oliver, 7, Shoreham by Sea

Amira, 13, London

Stanley, 10, Leigh on Sea

Maya, 10, Grayshott

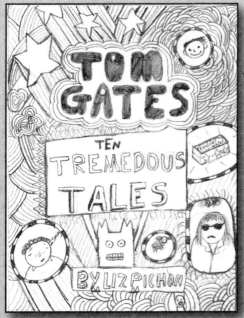

Jennifer, 12, Lincolnshire

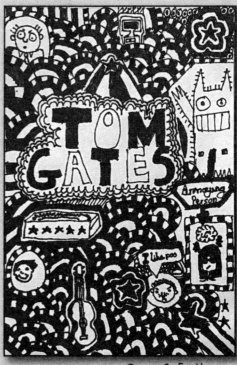

Oscar, 9, Eastbourne

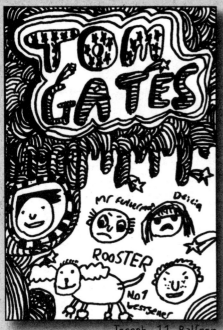

Joseph, 11, Balfron

Hammam, 11, Sale

Sara, 11, London

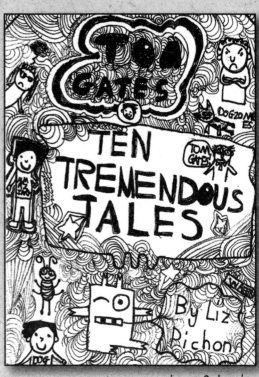

Lana, 9, London

ANSWERS

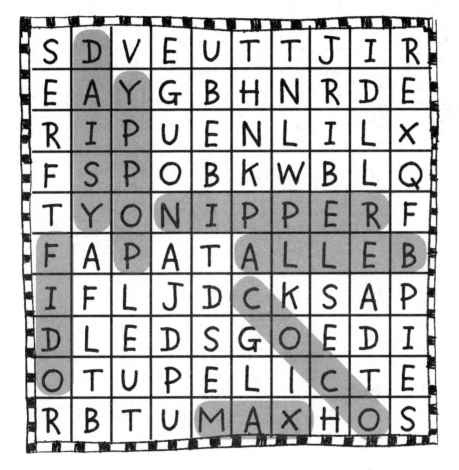

S	D	V	E	U	T	T	T	J	I	R
E	A	Y	G	B	H	N	R	D	E	E
R	I	P	U	E	N	L	I	L	X
F	S	P	O	B	K	W	B	L	Q
T	Y	O	N	I	P	P	E	R	F
F	A	P	A	T	A	L	L	E	B
I	F	L	J	D	C	K	S	A	P
D	L	E	D	S	G	O	E	D	I
O	T	U	P	E	L	I	C	T	E
R	B	T	U	M	A	X	H	O	S

Word search from page 29

Help Marcus through the maze

Marcus maze from pages 34 - 35

D	Y	P	W	K	J	U	R	S	D
F	R	O	O	S	T	E	R	D	O
S	E	P	J	B	O	I	A	E	G
F	A	P	M	A	A	C	N	L	Z
E	Y	T	O	M	P	B	T	I	O
I	W	R	N	D	D	S	A	A	M
S	O	M	S	A	R	M	G	L	B
H	D	I	T	G	G	T	E	D	I
A	Y	N	E	E	L	I	A	T	E
R	M	A	R	C	U	S	H	S	S

Word search from page 101

June and Amy's maze from pages 104 - 105

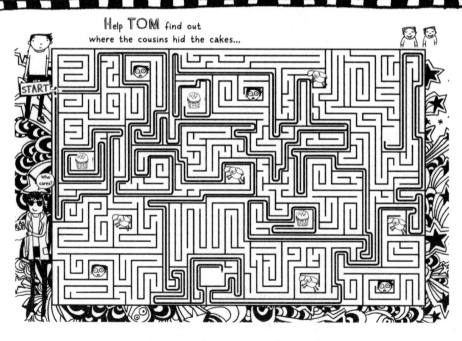

Tom's maze from pages 134 - 135